Cheshire Poets

Edited By Sadia Mahmood

First published in Great Britain in 2017 by:

Young Writers
Remus House
Coltsfoot Drive
Peterborough
PE2 9BF
Telephone: 01733 890066
Website: www.youngwriters.co.uk

SB ISBN 978-1-78820-427-9
Printed and bound in the UK by BookPrintingUK
Website: www.bookprintinguk.com
YB0327Y

Foreword

Dear Reader,

Welcome to this book packed full of feathery,
furry and scaly friends!

Young Writers' Poetry Safari competition was specifically designed
for 5-7 year-olds as a fun introduction to poetry and as a way to
think about the world of animals. They could write about pets,
exotic animals, dinosaurs and you'll even find a few crazy
creatures that have never been seen before! From this starting
point, the poems could be as simple or as elaborate as the writer
wanted, using imagination and descriptive language.

Given the young age of the entrants, we have tried to include as
many poems as possible. Here at Young Writers we believe that
seeing their work in print will inspire a love of reading and writing
and give these young poets the confidence to develop their skills
in the future. Poetry is a wonderful way to introduce young
children to the idea of rhyme and rhythm and helps learning and
development of communication, language and literacy skills.

These young poets have used their creative writing abilities,
sentence structure skills, thoughtful vocabulary and most
importantly, their imaginations, to make their poems and the
animals within them come alive. I hope you enjoy reading them as
much as we have.

Sadia Mahmood

Contents

Zain Shakoor (7)	57
Sienna Lee Humphries (7)	58
Rory Cannock (7)	59
Darsh Vij (7)	60
Charlie Matthew Tucker (7)	61
Umsha Hussain (6)	62
Yuvraj Singh (7)	63
Xander Lee (6)	64
James Holt (6)	65
Celine Meric (7)	66
Dylan Holland (6)	67
Melissa Hargreaves (6)	68
Sienna Ward (6)	69
Isaac Hindmarsh (7)	70
Jasper Oliver Hughes (7)	71
Calum William Isbister (7)	72
Zena Sheth (6)	73
Emily Annabel Mary Allen (6)	74
Aarush Sud (6)	75
Faizan Khan (6)	76
Alana Sofia Jinks (6)	77

St Albans RC Primary School, Warrington

Rima Sheejo (6)	78
Bethany Baker (6)	79
Ola Hildebrandt (6)	80
Millierose Thomson (6)	81
Julia Krociel (6)	82
Evie Savage (6)	83
Kiean Earl Viar (6)	84
Oliver Sherratt (6)	85
Xander Mark Bradley (6)	86
Shreyansh Ranjan (6)	87
Brandon Chambers (6)	88
Chaitan Singh (6)	89
Alfie James McNicholas (6)	90
Aleksander Gniecki (6)	91

Tushingham-With-Grindley CE Primary School, Tushingham

Cherry Rose Langley (7)	92
Maddie Crabb (5)	94
Daisy Holland Hewlett (6)	96
Alice Snaith (7)	97
Amelia May Lloyd (5)	98
Callum Devaney (7)	99
Ralph Cornwell (7)	100
William Alexander Beattie (7)	101
Samuel L. J. Wilkinson (6)	102
Olivia Lewis (5)	103
Alexis Jayde Brookes (4)	104
Teya Mary Wood (6)	105
Oliver Devaney (4)	106
Darragh Cronin (7)	107
Joseph Brown (6)	108
Ethan Dooris (7)	109
Sylvie Cornwell (5)	110
Josie Bella Faithfull (6)	111
Joshua J. D. Wilkinson (5)	112
Rebecca Lewis (6)	113
Georgia Paul (5)	114
Molly Zella Davies (3)	115
Harry Jack Probin (4)	116
Harry Smith (7)	117
Orian Oak Thelwell Wood (5)	118
Gabriel Jenkins (7)	119
Alfie Dratwinski (4)	120
Holly Shrimplin (6)	121
Max Llewelyn Williams (5)	122
Conor Loud (4)	123
Elsa Dratwinska (6)	124
Roman Jenkins (4)	125
Oliver Alldridge (3)	126

The Poems

A Friend In My Life

Bears are fun to play with.
Humans smile and laugh,
Playing and laughing until they come to a
shop.
A shop to fill your dreams with.
Cats, dogs, hamsters too,
Then I saw a bear.
My dream came true.
My life with my bear is truly hard to
compare.

Emma Morrison (7)

Barrow CE Primary School, Great Barrow

The Chicken

I am brown and small you know
And I like it in the snow.
There are lots of corn to eat on trees
And in the cold, I will always sneeze.
I sprint because I am happy
And my wings are very flappy.

Freddie O'Flynn (7)
Barrow CE Primary School, Great Barrow

What's My Animal?

My animal has long legs.
My animal has two bulbous body parts.
My animal has four small eyes.
My animal eats flies.
My animal lives in a web.
What's my animal?

Lacey Clegg (6)

Hallwood Park Primary School & Nursery, Hallwood Park
Estate

The Kitty Cat

No one lets me pick her up.
Is she quieter than any other cat?
She plays with her favourite ball
But I miss her so much.
She is adorable.

Macie McDonald (6)

Hallwood Park Primary School & Nursery, Hallwood Park
Estate

My Glorious Giraffe

She has a lovely long neck like a snake.
She has a wiggly tail like a worm.
She runs as fast as a flash.
She munches and crunches leaves.

Kelsey Roberts (5)
Hallwood Park Primary School & Nursery, Hallwood Park Estate

Hi Five Bear

He is furry and fluffy with big blue eyes
He eats fish in his dark cave
He snores when he sleeps
And chases butterflies to play with.

Paddy O'Neill (6)

Hallwood Park Primary School & Nursery, Hallwood Park
Estate

My Favourite Cat

My cat is cute, furry, white and soft
She sips her milk and nibbles her food.
Miaow, miaow, purr, purr
This cat is mine.

Jacob Jones-Williams (6)

Hallwood Park Primary School & Nursery, Hallwood Park
Estate

The Lion Poacher

Lions are good at chasing other animals.
Lions run like Sonic.
Lions have mighty roars!
Lions can hear lots of things.

Jasmine Jean Loney (6)
Hallwood Park Primary School & Nursery, Hallwood Park
Estate

Cuddly Cats

Cats are very sneaky.
My cat is tortoiseshell.
She likes to hunt.
She can pounce
But keep her away from dogs!

Grace Johnston (6)
Hallwood Park Primary School & Nursery, Hallwood Park Estate

My Gorgeous Hippo

Hippos have...
Pink eyes,
Enormous mouths,
Tiny ears
And they have lovely stompy feet!

Connor Houghton (6)

Hallwood Park Primary School & Nursery, Hallwood Park
Estate

Dolphin

Smooth blue skin.
Tiny teeth eating tiny fish.
Gigantic tails and fins.

Olly Higham (6)

Hallwood Park Primary School & Nursery, Hallwood Park Estate

Big Giraffe

G rass is their favourite food
I love it too
R eally tall
A ll giraffes have long necks
F eeds on fresh grass
F unny and playful
E ats grass and leaves off the tree.

Funny and happy, playful and fun
And playing with his friend.
Giraffes are a very tall animal.

Phoebe Dickson (5)

Havannah Primary School, Buglawton

Cheeky Cheetah

C heetahs are spotty.

H e is big.

E very cheetah is quick.

E very cheetah is strong.

T ime to stop running. Cheetahs

A re strong. They live in a

H ot place.

Charlie Taylor (6)

Havannah Primary School, Buglawton

Penguin

P enguins peck a lot.

E ggs.

N ow live in Antarctica.

G ood swimmers.

U sually thick fur. There

I s colour on their beaks.

N ice friends.

Milo Hopkin (5)
Havannah Primary School, Buglawton

Cheetah

C reeps up on their enemies

H ot place

E ats meat

E normous animals

T ough teeth

A round hot air

H e runs at 50 miles per hour.

Tristan James Green (6)

Havannah Primary School, Buglawton

George The Chameleon

Chameleons change colour.
Hungry ants meander.
Every chameleon changes colour
And has long legs.
Everyone loves chameleons.
Olives, neon-green.

Khy Waterhouse (6)
Havannah Primary School, Buglawton

Snake

S lither for food

N ever eat leaves

A ll snakes sniff for food

K ing to their friends

E very snake has a tail.

Willow-Grace Joan Beresford (5)

Havannah Primary School, Buglawton

The Tall Giraffe

Green giraffes are poorly.
In Africa is where you will find them.
Ants for dinner.
Furry creatures.
Friendly as a dog.
Enormous neck.

Logan Colbridge (5)
Havannah Primary School, Buglawton

Lions

L ions are fearless
I n the night the lions roar
O n a rock they sleep
N ow at 10 o'clock they wake up.

Olivia Ford (5)
Havannah Primary School, Buglawton

Spider

S cary spider
P oisonous
I s creepy
D ark black hair
E ats crickets
R uns very fast.

Thomas Dale (6)
Havannah Primary School, Buglawton

Snake

S limy
N aughty
A te a fish?
K ind
E very snake is fun.

Jodie Henstock (6)
Havannah Primary School, Buglawton

Mrs Fox

F oxes have bushy tails,
O range coloured
e X cept lonely, sly Mrs Fox.

Lexie Finney (6)
Havannah Primary School, Buglawton

Wild Carp

C arps are slimy!
A re they lonely?
R apid!
P owerful!

Tyler James Barnett (6)
Havannah Primary School, Buglawton

Black Mamba

B lack mambas are as cold as ice,
L ike to slither and shake,
A dangerous animal with poisonous fangs,
C an eat an animal without chewing it.
K ills prey as fast as the blink of an eye.

M an beware because it likes man best,
A black mamba kills anything in its sight,
M ay even kill another snake if very hungry,
B y half a second its prey's dead.
A black mamba can eat anything from
human to elephant.

Yaroslav Shemanov (7)
Lady Barn House School, Langlands

My Bunny Poem

My pet, Daisy, hops all about.
My pet, Daisy, gets frightened
when people shout.
Daisy smells as fresh as a rose.
Daisy tastes young plants, green grass,
yummy cabbage and orange carrots.
Daisy feels as soft as a feather.
Whenever she sees something orange
she checks if it's a carrot.
Daisy's eyes are as small as a button.

Amanah Faraz Malik (6)

Lady Barn House School, Langlands

An Unusual Unicorn

It's as magical as Hermione Granger.
It's as pretty as Ginny Weasley.
It's as kind as Professor McGonagall.
It's as gentle as Lilly Potter.
It's as wonderful as Luna Lovegood.
It has wings that shine in the sun.
It has a horn that shimmers like gold.
It's a flying unicorn.

Ayana Bilal (7)
Lady Barn House School, Langlands

My Rabbit Cuddles

My rabbit's cuddles feel as fluffy as a cloud.
My rabbit's cuddles smell as fresh as the sky.
My rabbit's cuddles sound as loud as a firework.
My rabbit's cuddles taste like candyfloss.
My rabbit's cuddles look like the snow.
My rabbit's cuddles are the best rabbit cuddles ever.

Suleiman Omar (6)

Lady Barn House School, Langlands

My Cheetah Poem

A cheetah tastes of chewy meat and blood.
He smells of gone-off meat and grass.
He sounds sometimes snarly
And sometimes as quiet as a mouse.
My cheetah is as sleek as a jet,
Very smooth and like a laminated sheet.
He looks like banana sauce
With chocolate drops, cunning and fierce.

Matthew Whitehurst (7)
Lady Barn House School, Langlands

Giant Giraffe

It's as tall as a skyscraper.
It's as slow as a snail.
Its feet are as loud as an explosion!
It's as big as an elephant.
It's as spotty as a cheetah.
It's amazing like a water park
And its neck is as tall as a drainpipe.
It's a giraffe.

Xander Kruger (6)
Lady Barn House School, Langlands

My Rabbit Poem

My rabbit is called Fast,
Because she hops very fast.
Fast is very busy,
She is busy as a bumblebee.
She feels soft, cuddly and furry as can be.
She sounds like a car hopping around.
Fast likes eating young plants and
cabbages.
She loves me, I love her.

Ava Lin (6)
Lady Barn House School, Langlands

My Parrot Poem

Parrots smell of feathers and nuts,
All soft and cuddly.
Parrots look colourful but they're loud!
Parrots sound like lightning and squawking.
Parrots feel warm and have sharp claws,
Just like the knives in the kitchen.
Parrots taste like hot meat.

Jibreel Choudhury (7)
Lady Barn House School, Langlands

Clever Chameleon

He's as scaly as a crocodile.
He's as multicoloured as a rainbow.
He's as quiet as a mouse.
He's that camouflaged that you won't see him coming,
He's always in my attic.
He's in Chester Zoo.
He's a chameleon.

Rani Kumar (7)
Lady Barn House School, Langlands

My Cheetah

My cheetah lives in the forest.
Its prey is birds and antelopes.
It hides in a tree.
It's as sly as a fox.
The cheetah is as fast as light.
It's as yellow as the sun.
The cheetah smells grassy.
It feels as smooth as a book.

Saara Sadiq (6)
Lady Barn House School, Langlands

My Tiger Poem

Tigers taste of meat, fur and crunchy bones.
Tigers smell of mud, grass and leaves.
Tigers look fierce, brave and strong.
Tigers sound as loud as an elephant
Stomping and as noisy as fireworks.
Tigers feel as soft as a fluffy white cloud.

Anushka Prasad (7)
Lady Barn House School, Langlands

Delightful Dog

He's as fluffy as a furball.
He's as small as a mouse.
He's as sweet as a peach.
He has eyes as big as two black buttons.
He makes me happier than a teacher with a silent class.
He sleeps like a log.
He's my dog!

Helena Berridge (7)
Lady Barn House School, Langlands

My Giraffe

My pet giraffe is as cute as a bunny.
My pet giraffe is as tall as a tree.
My pet giraffe is as quiet as a snail.
My pet giraffe smells as fresh as a daisy.
My pet giraffe tastes like leaves.
My pet giraffe feels as soft as a pillow.

Zeal Jimit Sheth (6)
Lady Barn House School, Langlands

My Sheep Poem

Sheep smell like grass and Chewbacca.
Sheep look like fluffy clouds on black stilts.
Sheep sound very happy
But they also sound annoying.
Sheep feel soft
And woolly like a jumper.
Sheep taste juicy
And also very chewy.

Sriram Muthukrishnan (7)

Lady Barn House School, Langlands

Beautiful Butterfly

She is as beautiful as a unicorn.
She is as small as an insect.
She is as colourful as a rainbow.
She has wings like a bird.
She is as rare as a robin.
She is as silky as a spider's silk.
She is a silky butterfly.

Emma Adams (6)
Lady Barn House School, Langlands

Pet Penguin

P riya my penguin is as pretty as a princess.

E pic as a wizard.

N ice as a panda.

G ood as a koala bear.

U nbelievable.

I t's as cute as a kitten.

N ever gets in the way.

Sara Anand (7)

Lady Barn House School, Langlands

The Unicorn

U nbelievable animal
N ever evil
I t's as beautiful as a rainbow
C ute as a kitten
O h how wonderful they are
R eally I think nobody should hate them
N obody hates them.

Esme Birkett (7)

Lady Barn House School, Langlands

My Puppy Poem

Puppies smell of sweet honey.
Puppies look like lots of different things.
Puppies are as golden as treasure.
Puppies sound like a banging drum.
Puppies feel like fluffy teddy bears.
Puppies taste of chocolate buttons.

Eva May Kaligotla (7)
Lady Barn House School, Langlands

Spooky, Spiky Shark

He lives in the sea.
He loves to swim a lot.
He is scarier than a dragon.
He smells like my dad.
His favourite snack is fish.
He is more amazing than Laser Quest
And he can swim very fast.
He is a shark.

Qasim Abbas Syed (7)
Lady Barn House School, Langlands

My Lion Poem

Lions smell like bloody grass,
Fresh as raindrops.
Lions look deadly and very fierce.
Lions sound as loud as thunder.
Lions feel very cuddly and warm.
Lions taste like meat with grass.
Lions look very sneaky.

Lucian Cystennin Jones (6)

Lady Barn House School, Langlands

The Super Fast Cheetah

He's as dangerous as a shark.
He's as fast as the wind.
He lives in the zoo.
He leaps as high as trees.
He's as yellow as the sun.
He's as spotty as a giraffe.
He is a cheetah.

Ali Ahmad (7)

Lady Barn House School, Langlands

Fantastic Flamingos

Flamingos smell like strawberries.
Flamingos' legs look like candy canes.
Flamingos sound like they're talking.
Flamingos feel like a very soft blanket.
Flamingos taste of ice cream sundaes.

Maria Hanif (6)
Lady Barn House School, Langlands

Cheetah Senses Poem

Cheetahs smell fresh and clean.
Cheetahs look like a fast travelling train.
Cheetahs sound like a growling tummy.
Cheetahs feel like a bed.
Cheetahs taste of ice cream that is melting on a hot day.

Alexander Jack (6)
Lady Barn House School, Langlands

My Elephant Poem

Elephants smell muddy and watery.
Elephants look fat, old and wrinkly.
Elephants sound like a bored goat
and shaking trees.
Elephants feel soft and cuddly.
Elephants taste like grass and mud.

Ella Chopra (7)
Lady Barn House School, Langlands

Ely The Elephant

It's as big as a dragon.
It's as kind as my sister.
It's as cheeky as a chimpanzee.
It's as cuddly as a teddy bear.
It's as cute as a rose.
It's my baby elephant.

Manaal Christmas (7)
Lady Barn House School, Langlands

My Dog Poem

A dog feels soft and warm
Just like I feel in my bed.
A dog sounds like a crackling bonfire.
A dog tastes like ice cream.
A dog smells of mud and grass.
A dog looks friendly and cute.

Freddie Mulcock (7)

Lady Barn House School, Langlands

My Polar Bear Poem

My polar bear looks very cuddly
But a bit scary
And it is very big.
It tastes as cold as an ice cream
And very salty.
It sounds very grizzly and hungry.
It smells like a stinky seal.

Lottie Winterton (6)
Lady Barn House School, Langlands

Penguin

She is as soft as a bear.
She is as sweet as a peach.
She loves to eat fish.
She is great at diving.
She tastes like ice.
She smells like peppermints.
She is a penguin.

Kaitlin Hoi Lum Au (7)

Lady Barn House School, Langlands

Dolphin Sense Poem

Dolphins smell fishy like the dining room on fish Friday.
Dolphins look like a fish swimming across the sea.
Dolphins feel all smooth and slippery.
Dolphins taste of salty crisps.

Darcey Greenwood (6)

Lady Barn House School, Langlands

My Dolphin Poem

Dolphins feel wet, smooth and slimy.
Dolphins taste amazing and delicious.
Dolphins are fresh and fishy.
Dolphins sound squeaky and noisy.
Dolphins look friendly and bright.

Martha Staines (7)
Lady Barn House School, Langlands

Beautiful Unicorn

She is as cute as a button.
She is as sweet as a teddy.
She is as cheeky as a monkey.
She is as fluffy as a feather.
Her horn is like a rainbow.
She is a unicorn.

Ameliah Gill (7)
Lady Barn House School, Langlands

My Best Monkey

The monkey swings through the trees.
Then he falls down into the leaves.
He likes swinging through the leaves.
He scares his mother every day.
He really likes bananas.

Harrison Webster (6)
Lady Barn House School, Langlands

Dogs Senses Poem

Dogs smell like plain crisps.
Dogs look like sausages in a bun.
Dogs sound like barking.
Dogs taste like meat with hair on.
Dogs feel like soft sheep's wool.

Pierce Alexander (6)

Lady Barn House School, Langlands

Scary Scorpion

It's as black as the Batcave in Chester Zoo.
It's as bumpy as a rock.
Its sting stings like a bee.
It's as long as a centipede.
It's a scorpion.

Zain Shakoor (7)
Lady Barn House School, Langlands

My Cat Poem

Cats smell of fish and they are swell.
Cats are the best animals you can get.
My cat tastes like meat.
My cat feels as cuddly as a polar bear.
My cat smells milky.

Sienna Lee Humphries (7)

Lady Barn House School, Langlands

Tasty Tiger

He smells of leaves from the trees.

He is as fluffy as a fox.

He is as dangerous as a polar bear.

He likes to taste raw meat.

He sounds like thunder when he roars.

Rory Cannock (7)

Lady Barn House School, Langlands

Charming Chameleon

He is a weird animal.
He lives in a jungle.
He is cuddly.
He is soft.
He climbs on trees.
He changes his colours like traffic lights.
He is a chameleon.

Darsh Vij (7)
Lady Barn House School, Langlands

The Scary Lion

L ikes to eat random things.

I ts teeth are stronger than iron.

O n its back it has blood.

N ow in the middle of the day they hunt for food.

Charlie Matthew Tucker (7)
Lady Barn House School, Langlands

Cats Sense Poem

Cats smell like a dusty summer's day.
Cats look as cute as me.
Cats sound like *miaow, purr, yawn.*
Cats feel cuddly.
Cats taste like tuna fish.

Umsha Hussain (6)

Lady Barn House School, Langlands

Pet Poem

Cats taste of strawberries all so yummy.
Cats smell like ham and sausages.
Cats look scared.
Cats feel fluffy, soft and warm.
Cats sound alone in England.

Yuvraj Singh (7)

Lady Barn House School, Langlands

My Dog, Frankie

She looks as fluffy as a ball of cotton wool.
She yelps as loud as fireworks.
She smells like a rotten banana.
Her breath smells as bad as a bowl of dog food.

Xander Lee (6)

Lady Barn House School, Langlands

Hungry Muncho

It's as cute as a bunny.
It's as hungry as a bear.
It's as slow as a snail.
It's as sad as a teacher in a noisy room.
It's a muncho!

James Holt (6)
Lady Barn House School, Langlands

Monkey

M onkeys are cheeky.
O rangey-brown.
N aughty as a cheetah.
K iwi shaped.
E lephant friends.
Y ellow coloured.

Celine Meric (7)
Lady Barn House School, Langlands

Dangerous Dragon

He's taller than an elephant.
His breath stinks as bad as a stink bomb.
He has big red eyes
His favourite food is rabbit.
He's very scary.

Dylan Holland (6)
Lady Barn House School, Langlands

Noisy Horses Sense Poem

Horses smell sweet like cakes.
Horses look like a big bar of chocolate.
Horses feel all smooth and silky.
Horses taste of smoked salmon!

Melissa Hargreaves (6)

Lady Barn House School, Langlands

Dolphin

She is so smooth and beautiful.
She had a breathing problem.
She can also speak to me.
She is also allergic to underwater things.

Sienna Ward (6)
Lady Barn House School, Langlands

Untitled

It's as green as grass.
Underneath it is smooth.
It has rotten breath.
It smells like blood.
My animal is a crocodile.

Isaac Hindmarsh (7)
Lady Barn House School, Langlands

Delightful Dog

It's as loud as a lion.
It's as cheeky as a monkey.
It's as greedy as a seagull.
It's my pet dog.

Jasper Oliver Hughes (7)
Lady Barn House School, Langlands

The Big Lion

L ong and he can roar
I n a cage
O h he's scared
'N o more,' I said to him.

Calum William Isbister (7)
Lady Barn House School, Langlands

A Simile Poem About A Bunny

As fluffy as a cloud.
As cute as a mouse.
As hoppy as a kangaroo.
As short as a white pompom.

Zena Sheth (6)
Lady Barn House School, Langlands

A Simile Poem About A Cheetah

As fast as lightning.
Spotty as a leopard.
Smelly as rotten fish.
Claws as sharp as needles.

Emily Annabel Mary Allen (6)

Lady Barn House School, Langlands

A Sense Poem About A Fox

Foxes smell like a skunk.

Foxes look as orange as the sunset.

A fox feels as fluffy as a feather.

Aarush Sud (6)

Lady Barn House School, Langlands

Simile Poem About An Octopus

As squashy as a ball.
As skinny as paper.
As smelly as fish.
As long as a twig.

Faizan Khan (6)
Lady Barn House School, Langlands

Panda Haiku

It lives in China,
Likes to eat scrumptious bamboo.
It is black and white.

Alana Sofia Jinks (6)
Lady Barn House School, Langlands

A Tiger

The tiger's colour is orange like a sunset.
Its skin is smooth and furry
And when you touch her it can feel soft too.
She sounds terrifying, scary and unkind.
She lives in the hot, green jungle
With terrible creatures living in it.
It sometimes eats big animals
And cute looking baby mice.

Rima Sheejo (6)
St Albans RC Primary School, Warrington

The Parrot

The parrot's wings are graceful
and colourful.
His feathers are like soft candyfloss.
While he is flying through the bright blue
sky he sounds as loud as an avalanche.
He lives in the garden jungle up,
up in the treetops.
He eats tiny brown nuts and juicy berries.

Bethany Baker (6)
St Albans RC Primary School, Warrington

The Monkey

The monkey looks silly
And crazy when he's happy.
The monkey feels soft and hairy like a kiwi.
The monkey lives in the green jungle.
The monkey eats yellow bananas like the
sun.
The monkey sounds funny and excited.

Ola Hildebrandt (6)

St Albans RC Primary School, Warrington

A Polar Bear

He eats baby fish and golden fish.
He looks like a grumpy teddy.
He lives in the coldest place
in the whole world.
He feels soft like a rabbit.
He sounds like a lion when
he's chasing his food.

Millierose Thomson (6)
St Albans RC Primary School, Warrington

Monkey

He looks like the happiest monkey in the
zoo.
He has the hairiest hands I have ever seen.
He sounds noisy when he is giggling.
He lives in the zoo in England.
He eats bananas as yellow as the sun.

Julia Krociel (6)
St Albans RC Primary School, Warrington

Snake

The snake is as colourful as a rainbow
And is as long as a measuring tape.
Its scales are as dry as paper.
Hisssss.
Like a balloon, when you let it go
It flies around the room.

Evie Savage (6)
St Albans RC Primary School, Warrington

The Parrot

She is as beautiful as a princess.
She feels as feathery as a duster.
She copies what we say when we speak.
She lives on the top of a tree as tall as a mountain.
She eats little tiny seeds.

Kiean Earl Viar (6)

St Albans RC Primary School, Warrington

The Tiger

Looks like a stripy tie.
Feels as soft as a teddy bear
But I would not like a hug.
Courageous and fierce
When he is fighting another tiger.
Lives in the wild where the birds sing.

Oliver Sherratt (6)
St Albans RC Primary School, Warrington

Tigers

The tiger looks stripy and orange.
He looks really, really scary.
He is as soft as a sheep
But you would not want a hug.
The tiger is really quiet.
The tiger eats bunnies.

Xander Mark Bradley (6)

St Albans RC Primary School, Warrington

The Polar Bears

He looks like a white snow monster.
He feels like a furry dog.
His growl is as loud as a lion.
He lives in a land as cold as ice.
He eats small, scaly, shimmery fish.

Shreyansh Ranjan (6)
St Albans RC Primary School, Warrington

Snake

The snake is as colourful as a rainbow
And as long as a bridge.
Its scales are as dry as sand.
Hisses like a balloon flying around a room.
The snake lives in a hole.

Brandon Chambers (6)
St Albans RC Primary School, Warrington

The Tigers

He's as stripy as a zebra.
He feels soft like a kitten but he's scarier.
He lives in the mountain as big as a giant!
He's fierce when he's fighting.

Chaitan Singh (6)
St Albans RC Primary School, Warrington

The Polar Bear

It looks as white as snow.
It feels soft like beds.
It sounds as loud as a panda.
It lives in the chilly Antarctica.
It nibbles large fish.

Alfie James McNicholas (6)
St Albans RC Primary School, Warrington

Parrots

He is as colourful as a flower.
He feels soft like a bed.
He squawks loudly
Because he is a chatterbox.
He lifts up a massive green tree.

Aleksander Gniecki (6)

St Albans RC Primary School, Warrington

The Laughing Hyenas

His body is curved and squat,
He's light brown and covered in spots.
He's a powerful hunter with massive sharp
teeth.
He has four squishy pads and claws on his
feet.
His name is Henry, his friends are in the
clan,
They're called Harry, Hetty and another
called Stan.
They all live together in the African
savannah,
Henry certainly has not got good manners.
For dinner he mainly eats meat,
But he's not so fussy on wheat.
One day, they all went hunting,
There definitely won't be any bunting.
They ate their supper,
There really wasn't any need for butter.

They went to bed with their favourite ted
And said goodnight to the savannah.

Cherry Rose Langley (7)
Tushingham-With-Grindley CE Primary School, Tushingham

Bert The Friendly Lion

There once was a lion called Bert,
He wore a colourful shirt.
Underneath he was kind, funny and hairy.
However, he was not very scary.

For his dinner Bert ate wasps, grass and
flowers.
Bert ate them for hours and hours and
hours.
Bert lived in a pretty pink house
Which was as quiet as a mouse.

Bert's house was to be found in the
mountains,
In the garden there were hundreds of
fountains.
The fountains were handy because Bert like
a bath.
He would make lots of bubbles which gave
him a laugh.

Now Bert had six legs
That did not look like pegs
But were useful for kicking a ball
Especially when Bert was so small.

Maddie Crabb (5)
Tushingham-With-Grindley CE Primary School, Tushingham

Dreams Of Tiger

In my dreams he is bold and strong.
We fly and jump from cloud to cloud,
Gliding, soaring, we are not boring.
In my dreams we canter so fast
The sand punches the air
And falls silently like fairy dust.
The tiger's hooves beat like drums,
A dance of delight.
In my dreams we look after each other,
Sharing, caring, loving life.
In my dreams he carries me safely home
Without a doubt.
Dreams always come true with my tiger.

Daisy Holland Hewlett (6)
Tushingham-With-Grindley CE Primary School, Tushingham

A Tasty Treat

Jonny the meerkat popped out of his
burrow,
'I'm off to the shops, I'll see you tomorrow!
I'm tired of the same old insects to eat.
There must be something better, can't I
have a treat?'
Bright and alert, Jonny sniffed the air,
Surely there's something more tasty out
there?
'Scorpions I smell, juicy and spicy,
Deep fried in batter, that will do nicely!'

Alice Snaith (7)

Tushingham-With-Grindley CE Primary School, Tushingham

Animals In The Crazy Jungle

Zebras' stripes are black and white.
All sorts of animals come alive at night.
Lions' teeth as sharp as glass,
Stalking prey while hiding in the grass.
Elephants stamp their big feet
While tigers eat some meat.
Parrots sing and talk all day,
Flitting through the trees,
How they love to play.
Monkeys swing from tree-to-tree,
Oh how happy they seem to be.

Amelia May Lloyd (5)

Tushingham-With-Grindley CE Primary School, Tushingham

I Wish I Could Go As Fast As A Cheetah

I'm creeping through the plains.
I see my prey nibbling on thin grass.
I'm creeping up silently towards my dinner.
I'm crouching in the long grass.
I'm launching to the moon to pounce on my prey.
I'm running, I'm speeding,
I'm zooming like a rocket!
My prey trips on a stone
And I've got my dinner!

Callum Devaney (7)
Tushingham-With-Grindley CE Primary School, Tushingham

My Lion

My lion is big
My lion is small
My lion once ate a twig
My lion once saw Darth Maul
My lion is hairy
My lion supports Burnley
My lion's wife is called Mary
My lion's favourite cricket bat is a Duncan
Fearnley
My lion has three cubs
Called Ryan, Solomon and James
My lion does cricket and football clubs.

Ralph Cornwell (7)
Tushingham-With-Grindley CE Primary School, Tushingham

The Monkey Dream

I'm a monkey, my name is Jack.
I love my food and like to snack.
I love to eat my seeds and fruit.
When I'm eating bananas I look really cute.
I live in the jungle with the flowers and
trees,
Lions and snakes, birds and bees.
Swinging through the trees day and night
Like a fluffy brown bear I'm a lovely sight.

William Alexander Beattie (7)
Tushingham-With-Grindley CE Primary School, Tushingham

Super Bird

S aves lives every day
U p and down he flies
P ellets shoot through the air
E xciting to rescue animals
R iding on his huge wings.

B right and colourful everywhere
I n the winter he flies south
R eally, really powerful
D igging to help trapped people.

Samuel L. J. Wilkinson (6)
Tushingham-With-Grindley CE Primary School, Tushingham

The Friendly Elephant

The huge, massive elephant
wandered through the desert,
his big ears flapping
and his long trunk swaying.
He reached up high into the green trees
with his long trunk, stretched out
to grab the tasty leaves.
The heavy elephant slowly stomped
towards his friend,
he finally got there in the end!

Olivia Lewis (5)
Tushingham-With-Grindley CE Primary School, Tushingham

My Lion

My lion is loud, my lion is scary.
My lion is pretty but also hairy.
My lion is my friend
And lives at my house.
She comes for tea
And eats the whole house.
We get her a treat, a big juicy bone.
She eats it all up
And then sleeps all day.
My lion is loud, my lion's called Rosie.

Alexis Jayde Brookes (4)

Tushingham-With-Grindley CE Primary School, Tushingham

When Elly Met Lilly

Elly the elephant lived in a herd
Until he met Lilly Ladybird.

'What a big elephant,' said Lilly to Elly.
'You are as small as an ant,' said Elly to Lilly.

'I'm off on a journey,
It's hot and it's sunny, safari, so goody!'

Teya Mary Wood (6)
Tushingham-With-Grindley CE Primary School, Tushingham

Oliver The Giraffe

A little giraffe called Oliver
lived in the jungle.
He had four legs, two eyes, two horns,
a really long neck and was covered in spots.
Oliver liked to play hide-and-seek
with his friends.
He hid in tall trees and ate all the leaves,
then ran back home to his mum.

Oliver Devaney (4)
Tushingham-With-Grindley CE Primary School, Tushingham

The Darting Jaguar

The darting jaguar sprints all about
With his powerful strong legs.
In the distance the jaguar spots a herd of
deer.
The spotty jaguar is on the hunt.
The jaguar sprints after the herd of jumping
deer.
He picks the fattest deer.
He darts and catches the deer.

Darragh Cronin (7)
Tushingham-With-Grindley CE Primary School, Tushingham

The Cheetah

The cheetah, is he spotty or not?
Is he hairy? Is he fast?
Is he colourful and slender?
In a race, would he come last?
Is he nice or not?
Is he fluffy? Is he kind?
Can he climb trees? We don't mind,
Because the cheetah is the fastest of them
all.

Joseph Brown (6)
Tushingham-With-Grindley CE Primary School, Tushingham

My Cheetah Poem

This is all about my cheetah,
He likes to eat pizza.
He's got black spots, yellow fur
And loves to purr.
He likes to run a lot
Very, very quickly.
He's the fastest animal of all,
But doesn't roar!
What an amazing cheetah he is!

Ethan Dooris (7)
Tushingham-With-Grindley CE Primary School, Tushingham

My Monkey

My monkey is cheeky,
He climbs on cars.
He lives in the desert,
He likes to eat chocolate bars.

My monkey is kind to me,
He isn't nice to other people
And when he is being really bad
He climbs up the church steeple!

Sylvie Cornwell (5)
Tushingham-With-Grindley CE Primary School, Tushingham

Honey Bunny

In a forest lived a fluffy, pretty bunny,
The bunny was looking for some yummy
honey
But where could it be?
Maybe it's on top of a rainbow.
Look a rainbow, the bunny has found his
honey.
Hooray, hooray, he can fill his tummy.

Josie Bella Faithfull (6)
Tushingham-With-Grindley CE Primary School, Tushingham

Twinkle-Toes

He is bright blue
He eats only dark chocolate
He eats only sharp leaves
He is kind and gentle

He likes kissing all people
He lives far away
He lives in a snowy, chilly place
He likes *me* most of all.

Joshua J. D. Wilkinson (5)
Tushingham-With-Grindley CE Primary School, Tushingham

I Met A Giraffe

I met a giraffe called Jack,
'Why are you so black?'
'Because I can camouflage in the night
So I can get away from tigers that bite.'
I left him eating his acacia tree,
The paint still dripping from his knee.

Rebecca Lewis (6)
Tushingham-With-Grindley CE Primary School, Tushingham

Mr Crocodile

Snap, snap, snap
Go the shiny white teeth.
Green scaly skin and a long pointy tail.
Swimming in the river,
Beware little fish, here he comes.
It's the crocodile,
Snap, snap, snap.

Georgia Paul (5)
Tushingham-With-Grindley CE Primary School, Tushingham

Stripy Zebra

Stripy zebra let's play,
Stripy zebra it's a sunny day,
You can play or have a drink,
Stripy zebra why aren't you pink?

Because I'm black and white!
Let's gallop and play.

Molly Zella Davies (3)
Tushingham-With-Grindley CE Primary School, Tushingham

My Cheetah

She hides in the jungle.
She is sleeping in a tree
When down below she hears a sound.
It's a lonely animal with no friends.
She bites him for her tea.
She goes to sleep now
Lying on the ground.

Harry Jack Probin (4)
Tushingham-With-Grindley CE Primary School, Tushingham

The Cheetah

The cheetah runs past,
He runs so fast
Following his prey,
To survive another day.
His beautiful spots glow
As bright as the sun.

I'm the fastest,
Catch me if you can.

Harry Smith (7)
Tushingham-With-Grindley CE Primary School, Tushingham

Tiger Love

Hunting in the jungle,
Stripy fur in the forest,
Growling sharp claws,
Long tail swishing,
Soft fur on tiger's tummy,
Sleeping in the sun full of love.

Orian Oak Thelwell Wood (5)

Tushingham-With-Grindley CE Primary School, Tushingham

George The Giraffe

George the giraffe
Had a very loud laugh.
When he walked he squawked and
squawked.
George laughed at his giraffe laugh
Because he couldn't talk.

Gabriel Jenkins (7)
Tushingham-With-Grindley CE Primary School, Tushingham

Monty The Monkey

Cheeky little monkey swinging in the tree,
Wanting bananas for his tea,
Playing with his friends,
He has fun,
Cute little monkey, how happy is he?

Alfie Dratwinski (4)

Tushingham-With-Grindley CE Primary School, Tushingham

Stripey The Zebra

There was a zebra called Stripey
He thought he was really posh
But every day he got dirty
And his stripes wouldn't come off in the wash!

Holly Shrimplin (6)
Tushingham-With-Grindley CE Primary School, Tushingham

My Lion

My lion lives in Africa.
He is a happy carnivore.
His eyes are yellow
Like the sun.
He runs and runs
And has lots of fun.

Max Llewelyn Williams (5)
Tushingham-With-Grindley CE Primary School, Tushingham

Elephant

Elephant, you are so grey,
We love you in a special way.
We love it when you like to boogie.
We all just have to move, move, move.

Conor Loud (4)
Tushingham-With-Grindley CE Primary School, Tushingham

Polly The Parrot

Polly the parrot flying high over the vast sea
As happy as can be.
She lands by a tall tree
And she noisily squawked at me.

Elsa Dratwinska (6)

Tushingham-With-Grindley CE Primary School, Tushingham

Willa The Gorilla

Willa was the silverback
Who owned the mountain stack.
He ate fruit and plants all day
And scratched his silver back!

Roman Jenkins (4)
Tushingham-With-Grindley CE Primary School, Tushingham

Oliver The Rhino

His middle name is Oya,
He stomps around the jungle.
His friends are the polar bears,
He always says hello.

Oliver Alldridge (3)
Tushingham-With-Grindley CE Primary School, Tushingham

Young Writers Information

We hope you have enjoyed reading this book – and that you will continue to in the coming years.

If you're a young writer who enjoys reading and creative writing, or the parent of an enthusiastic poet or story writer, do visit our website www.youngwriters.co.uk. Here you will find free competitions, workshops and games, as well as recommended reads, a poetry glossary and our blog.

If you would like to order further copies of this book, or any of our other titles give us a call or visit **www.youngwriters.co.uk**.

Young Writers, Remus House, Coltsfoot Drive, Peterborough, PE2 9BF
(01733) 890066

info@youngwriters.co.uk